QUANTUM COMPUT

QUANTUM COMPUTING

How It Works, and Why It Could
Change the World

Amit Katwala

1 3 5 7 9 10 8 6 4 2

Random House Business
20 Vauxhall Bridge Road
London SW1V 2SA

Random House Business is part of the Penguin Random House
group of companies whose addresses can be found at
global.penguinrandomhouse.com.

First published by Random House Business in 2021

Image on p. 15 © NekoJaNekoJa and Johannes Kalliauer.
Republished under the Creative Commons Attribution-Share
Alike 4.0 International license. https://commons.wikimedia.org/wiki/
File:Double-slit.svg

www.penguin.co.uk

A CIP catalogue record for this book is available from
the British Library.

ISBN 9781847943262

Typeset in 9.5/18 pt Exchange Text
by Integra Software Services Pvt. Ltd, Pondicherry

Printed and bound in Great Britain by Clays Ltd, Elcograf S.p.A

The authorised representative in the EEA is Penguin Random House
Ireland, Morrison Chambers, 32 Nassau Street, Dublin D02 YH68.

Penguin Random House is committed to a sustainable future for
our business, our readers and our planet. This book is made from
Forest Stewardship Council® certified paper.

Contents

Introduction

Summit, the IBM supercomputer at Oak Ridge National Laboratory in Tennessee, weighs three times more than a blue whale and fills the space of two tennis courts. It has 219 kilometres of cabling and can perform more than three quintillion calculations per second. In June 2019, it was crowned the world's fastest supercomputer for the second year in a row.

But around the same time as it claimed that prize, Summit was being secretly outdone – not by Sierra, its closest US rival, nor by Fugaku, a Japanese project touted to overtake it when it comes fully online in 2021. Instead, this vast machine was quietly beaten by a tiny chip no bigger than a thumbnail, in a small private research lab near the beach in Santa Barbara, California.

The chip, called Sycamore, was developed by researchers at the search giant Google. It forms the central part of a quantum computer – a new, fundamentally different type of device that works according to the laws of quantum physics.

Quantum computers have vast potential. They could eventually revolutionise everything from artificial intelligence to the development of new drugs. A working quantum computer could help create powerful new materials, turbocharge the fight against climate change and completely upend the cryptography that keeps our secrets safe. It would, as *Discover* magazine put it in the early days of research, be 'less a machine than a force of nature'.[1]

If their potential can be fully realised, these devices won't simply be more powerful versions of our existing computers. They work in a completely different way, which could enable them to do seemingly impossible things. Because their strengths are so alien to the way most of us perceive the universe, it can be difficult to explain them without resorting to slightly fuzzy analogies. But effectively, quantum computers could unlock a new set of abilities based on the new, deeper understanding of the universe that physicists have developed over the last century.

'Imagine you're playing chess and the rules are changed in your favour, enabling your rook an expanded range of moves,' write quantum scientist Michael Nielsen and software engineer Andy Matuschak, in an analogy that attempts to make something astonishingly complex comprehensible to the average person.[2] 'That extra flexibility might enable you to achieve checkmate much faster because you can get to new positions much more quickly.'

In certain situations, quantum computers could allow us to do things that are impossible right now, even with the power of a million supercomputers. Believe the hype, and we're on the verge of a new technological era, in which quantum computers will help us create more efficient travel routes, and crunch complex sums in scientific experiments. They'll potentially change the way banks analyse risk, and allow chemists and biologists to create detailed simulations of the natural world to develop new, more efficient materials and processes. 'This is one of the biggest technology jumps ever, in history,' says William Hurley (known as Whurley), tech entrepreneur and founder of Strangeworks, which is working to make quantum computing accessible to all. 'Computing will change more in the next ten years than it has in the last hundred.'

Until recently, there were doubts over whether quantum computers would ever actually work. Even now, some are still sceptical whether a practically useful version of a quantum computer will ever actually exist. They're incredibly difficult to build, presenting huge engineering, manufacturing and mathematical challenges. But, over the last twenty years, some of the world's biggest companies – Google, Amazon, Microsoft, IBM, Intel and others – have been racing to build working, practically useful quantum devices.

In the summer of 2019, a team of researchers at Google, who had spent the better part of a decade trying to build quantum computers, reached a milestone known as 'quantum supremacy'. The term, coined by the physicist John Preskill, describes the point at which a quantum computer can do something that the world's best classical computer could never do.

This seminal moment in the history of computing arrived on 13 June, when Google's Sycamore chip – chilled to a temperature colder than outer space – performed a series of complex calculations that would have taken the Summit supercomputer 10,000 years, in just 3 minutes and 20 seconds. It was a landmark moment. 'This is a wonderful achievement. The engineering here is just phenomenal,' Peter Knight, a physicist at Imperial College London, told *New Scientist* when the research paper was published a few months later.[3] 'It shows that quantum computing is really hard but not impossible. It is a stepping stone toward a big dream.'

It marked a fundamental moment: when quantum computing went from being neat theory to genuine possibility. Since Google's announcement, millions of dollars in funding have poured into the field from governments and venture capitalists.

Inside Google, they compare the achievement to the first flight by the Wright brothers at Kitty Hawk, which marked the birth of the aviation industry. 'There are people that literally think that the thing we did or the next steps are not possible,' says Google quantum hardware engineer Tony Megrant, who helped design and build the Sycamore chip. Others are less convinced. By the time the research was officially published, some of Google's rivals in the quantum race – particularly IBM – had started to cast some doubt on whether the Sycamore chip was actually as far ahead of Summit as the search giant had claimed. They argued that the task Google set was too narrow and specific to count as quantum supremacy.

But regardless of the technicalities, quantum supremacy is a huge technical achievement, and one that could mark a new era of technological process: the dawn of the Quantum Age. The real race, however, has only just begun. 'We've been working on the hardware aspect of this for ten years, so I always picture in my head the starting line of a race being at the top of a mountain,' Megrant says. 'We had to get up here to start the race.'

This book will tell the story of that race, and explore the myriad ways in which quantum computers could reshape the worlds of finance, medicine and politics, and further our understanding of the universe. But we'll start with the basics.

1
What is quantum computing?

Until very recently, every computer in the world – from the room-sized codebreakers of the 1940s to the tiny processor in your smartphone – worked in essentially the same way. The birth of silicon chips and semiconductors has driven unbelievable progress, but the underlying principles governing today's high-tech devices are exactly the same ones that Alan Turing and his colleagues worked with at Bletchley Park, the British codebreaking centre which gave rise to some of the first classical computers. They are the same ones that power everything that came in between, to the extent that even your creaking old desktop PC can theoretically do anything the Summit supercomputer can do (if you give it enough time and memory).

These classical computers all work using bits. Bits are basically tiny switches – they can be one of three different kinds, either valves, relays or transistors etched in silicon – that can be in the off position, represented by a 0, or in the on position, represented by a 1. Every song you play, YouTube video you watch and app you download is ultimately made up of some combination of these 1s and 0s.

This combination of 0s and 1s – on and off switches – is known as binary code. It worked fine when the things computers needed to do were simple. The number 2 in binary, for instance, is represented by the string 10, while 3 is 11 and 4 is 100. But as computer processes get more complex, the number of bits you need to encode them grows rapidly. For example, 15 is 1111, while 500 is 111110100.

Each element in that string of binary code requires a separate bit, which means a separate physical switch that can alternate between one and zero. The technological marvels of the computer age have been made possible by huge advances in our ability to make those switches smaller and more efficient, so we can cram more and more bits into the same amount of space.

But there are still things we can't do, even with millions of these chips and trillions of bits running together in a supercomputer like Summit. Bits are black and white, either/or. When things are uncertain or complex, you need a lot more bits to describe them, which means that some seemingly simple problems can become exponentially more difficult for normal computers to handle.

'Say we want to send you from the UK to fourteen cities in the US and work out the optimal path – my laptop can do that in a second,' says tech entrepreneur Whurley. 'But if I made it twenty-two cities, using the same algorithm and the same laptop, it would take two thousand years.' This is a classic example of what's called the travelling salesman problem: the kind of problem where the challenge grows exponentially with each added variable.

A classical device trying to plot the most efficient order in which to visit the cities has to check every single possible combination, so for every city you add to the journey, the amount of computing power balloons – 11 cities have 20 million routes between them, 12 cities have 240 million routes, 15 cities have more than 650 billion. Modelling complex interactions between molecules, as we need to do if we want to accurately simulate chemical reactions, or speed up the development of medicines, creates the same problem: with every variable you add, the challenge gets a lot bigger.

The American physicist Richard Feynman was one of the first to realise this. Feynman was something of a rock star in academic circles – he'd worked on the atomic bomb, won the Nobel Prize and done pioneering work on nanotechnology. With his long hair and outspoken manner, he'd even achieved the often impossible feat of breaking into the public consciousness – a 1999 poll ranked him as one of the ten most influential physicists of the twentieth century.

But, most importantly, he was also a leading voice in quantum mechanics – the study of the strange things that start to happen in physics when you get down to a really small scale. In 1981, he gave a couple of lectures – one at Caltech in Pasadena, the other at MIT in Boston – that marked the beginnings of the field of quantum computing.

A (very) brief history of quantum mechanics

For centuries, physicists viewed the universe as a kind of giant pool table where atoms bounced off each other at perfect angles, in geometric lines determined by their speed and angle of impact. Their theories dated back to the work of the seventeenth-century mathematician Isaac Newton, who codified them in his famous laws of motion and gravitation.

But around the dawn of the twentieth century, as physicists delved deeper into the inner workings of the atom, they started spotting things that didn't match up to our understanding of Newtonian physics or thermodynamics, which governs how substances behave as their temperature changes. Below a certain scale, the laws of the universe seemed to just stop.

The field of quantum mechanics sprang up to describe the strange behaviour of the particles that go to make up an atom. (Atoms, as a reminder, consist of a nucleus of protons and neutrons orbited by electrons). Sometimes, physicists discovered, electrons behave like continuous streams, spreading out like a beam of light. At other times, they seem to be broken down into individual 'packets' or 'quanta' (hence 'quantum physics'), which, far from being continuous, are limited to discrete values – like a car that can only go at 30mph or 40mph, but nothing in between, or water from a tap that emerges not as a stream but only as visible drops. And sometimes they can appear to be in both states simultaneously – in a phenomenon called quantum superposition.

The classic illustration of this is the 'double slit' experiment. Imagine you're standing facing a thin wall, with two vertical slits cut into it like windows, and that there's another wall behind it. Now, imagine you have a paintball gun, and that you're firing it at the wall in front of you, strafing back and forth like the muscled hero in a low-budget action movie. The wall in front of you would be covered in paint, of course, while the wall behind that would be completely clear except for two vertical strips of paint corresponding with the two gaps in the first wall.

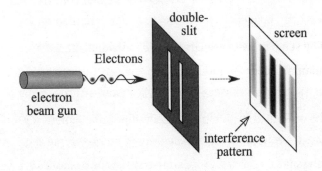

An illustration of the double slit experiment

But – and this is the bit that's basically driven the entire field of quantum physics for a century – if you were to shrink that experiment down and fire single electrons instead of paintballs, you'd find a completely different result.

Even if you'd fired the electron through one of those two slits, it would appear somewhere seemingly random on the back wall – not necessarily behind one of the two slits. Only after repeating this hundreds or thousands of times would a pattern start to emerge – one of alternating light and dark stripes, like a barcode. This pattern – called an interference pattern – happens because electrons seem to behave like waves until the point at which they're observed or measured, when they revert to being particles again.

When this initial electron wave passes through the two slits in the double-slit experiment, it creates two smaller waves, which then cancel out and reinforce each other. It's as if you'd dropped two stones into a pond and watched the ripples overlap and change one another. But these aren't real waves like the ones on the surface of still water. Instead of tracking the movement or behaviour of an object over time, these 'wave functions', as they're known, describe all the possible positions where an electron might be, and the varying probability of it occupying each position at a particular moment in time. When it's measured – in this case, when the electron hits the back wall – it's said that the wave function 'collapses' into a single specific outcome, like a spinning die coming to a stop. Physicists haven't yet explained how or why this happens, or indeed whether the wave function is simply a mathematical phenomenon, or something that actually happens in the real world in some observable way.

Imagine a textured map – like one of the world displaying features like the rise and fall of mountain ranges and valleys. Each point on the map represents a probability amplitude: the higher the terrain, the greater the likelihood of the electron occupying that position in space. The wave function in this analogy is the map itself – but it's a map that's capable of being twisted and distorted, like a wave of sound or water.

In the double-slit experiment, when this wave function hits the gaps in the front wall, it gets squeezed and compressed like a swell of water would. The different probability amplitudes that make up the wave function begin to interfere with one another in complex ways, as if you'd folded the textured map in half, or crunched it up into a ball.

The chance of an electron landing at a particular point on the back wall is determined by the way these probability amplitudes interfere with one another. In our normal lives, probability can only be a positive value – ranging from 0 per cent (impossible) to 100 per cent (certain). But in the quantum realm – the world of electrons and photons – probability can be 'positive, negative, or even complex', as Scott Aaronson, founding director of the Quantum Information Center at the University of Texas at Austin, explains in an article for the *New York Times*.[1] Where events at the classical scale have probabilities of between 0 and 1, at the quantum level, events have probability amplitudes instead – which can be either positive or negative.

This means that as well as reinforcing each other, these probability amplitudes can cancel one another out – so the event never happens at all, which explains the blank spaces in the barcode pattern of the double slit experiment. 'This is "quantum interference",' Aaronson writes, 'and it is behind everything else you've ever heard about the weirdness of the quantum world.'

At the atomic scale – the one we all live at – you can make specific, fairly accurate predictions about where an atom or an object will end up if you know its speed and direction. But these patterns of quantum interference mean that the subatomic scale has a degree of randomness baked in. You can only ever know the rough probability of something happening. You can never say for certain. The universe is not like a pool table. Nature has uncertainty baked into its core.

From bits to qubits

By the 1980s, early computers were beginning to be used for running simulations of the weather or chemical reactions, but Richard Feynman spotted the flaw. In order to accurately simulate physics, chemistry or anything else both complex and minuscule, you need a simulation that can adhere to the same, probability-based laws of quantum mechanics. Feynman summed up the problem at the end of one of his talks, which was on the challenges of simulating nature using computers, in a passage that's now part of quantum computing lore. 'Nature isn't classical, dammit, and if you want to make a simulation of nature, you'd better make it quantum mechanical,' he said. 'And, by golly, it's a wonderful problem, because it doesn't look so easy.'[2]

For a while, it was possible to sidestep Feynman's argument – at least in practical terms – because classical computers seemed to be advancing so quickly. In 1965, Intel's Gordon Moore formulated 'Moore's Law', which states that the number of transistors that can be crammed onto an integrated circuit (and with it the number of bits that can be processed) doubles roughly every two years. That has been the case for decades, and it's what has helped drive an era of astonishing technological progress. Packing smaller and more efficient transistors onto chips with increasingly elaborate structures has enabled computers with more storage, more memory and more power. They can run ever more powerful programs and simulations.

But in recent years, various problems have arisen. Transistors have become so small that we're starting to run into barriers. The first is energy. Adding more and more transistors makes chips ever more power-hungry, which means you need to either make each individual switch more efficient, or find a way of massively increasing the amount of power the computer uses. The second problem is heat. Although chipmakers do their best, the process of performing calculations inevitably generates heat, which requires ever more elaborate cooling systems.

The third problem is physics itself. Moore's Law is slowing down because, once you get to a really small scale, the laws of physics change, and quantum mechanics takes over. That means it's harder to make the kind of incremental improvements that have driven so much progress. In 2012,[3] Australian researchers created a transistor that consisted of a single atom, switching between two states to signify 1s and 0s. Today, transistors are being built that have features smaller than around 22 nanometres (for comparison, a human hair is about 80,000 nanometres thick).

Chipmakers have no choice but to grapple with quantum effects, as Google's Tony Megrant points out. Quantum physics will become an inevitable part of computing. 'As our field is just forming, you see an equal number of articles about the end of Moore's Law,' says Megrant. 'Things have been miniaturised so far that quantum effects are showing up. That's an error for them, whereas it's the thing we're harnessing.'

In 1985, the Oxford-based physicist David Deutsch went a step further than Feynman. Like Feynman, Deutsch has acquired almost legendary status in the world of quantum physics – he's famous for almost never being seen outside his house in Oxford, where he works

WHAT IS QUANTUM COMPUTING?

late into the night with his head in other worlds. Most of his work has been focused on the notion of the multiverse – the idea that our universe is just one of almost infinite parallel universes, with every possible future unfolding simultaneously in one of them. That includes everything from a universe that's identical to ours until the moment the coin you just flipped lands on heads instead of tails, to a universe where Earth wasn't hit by a comet and dinosaurs evolved into intelligent beings with cars and planes and microchips of their own.[7]

Deutsch realised that a computer built from quantum components could be so much more powerful than just a physics simulator. Instead of bits, which can only be 1 or 0, these components – which would eventually become known as quantum bits, or 'qubits' – can be 1, 0 or in a state of superposition where they are 'both 1 and 0 at the same time'.

That's the simple explanation, and it's the one you'll usually encounter in news articles and popular science books like this one. The truth is a little more complicated.

A qubit in superposition is not technically in both states at the same time. Instead, it's got some probability of being 1 and some probability of being 0 – and observing it causes it to 'collapse' into one of the two states, as when you reveal the result of a coin toss.

But in basic terms, you can think of qubits as a globe, with 1 at the North Pole, 0 at the South Pole, and superposition at an unspecified point somewhere else on the sphere. Or imagine a coin: if heads is 1 and tails is 0, then superposition is a spinning coin, laden with unrealised potential futures.

Qubits can hold more information, more efficiently, than bits. To describe the state of one qubit, you'd need at least two bits (0 on a qubit would be 00, 1 would be 11, and superposition would be 01 or 10). For two qubits, you'd need four bits, for three qubits eight bits, and so on. To describe the state of 300 qubits, you'd need more bits than there are atoms in the known universe. You'd need 72 billion gigabytes of classical computer memory to store as much information as the 53 qubits on Google's

Sycamore chip, for instance. 'This is an exponential growth of the numbers that we would have to keep track of to describe this quantum system,' explains Tony Megrant. 'This is the exponential power that you hear of in quantum computing.'

Deutsch figured out that a computer built of qubits instead of bits could use the uncertainty of quantum mechanics to its advantage. As well as simulating nature more efficiently, Deutsch realised, a machine made from qubits would also be able to handle uncertainty more efficiently, and tackle certain problems thousands or millions of times faster. Instead of trying out each path of a maze in turn, it could effectively go down every single path in parallel, at the same time. It's a bit like holding your finger in the pages of a choose-your-own-adventure book – and seeing the consequences of every decision point at once.

If multiple qubits are coupled together, their interference patterns can be carefully choreographed so that the paths leading to wrong answers cancel one another out, while those leading to the right answer reinforce one another. The result is an exponential increase in computing power for certain types of problem. This is why some believe that quantum computers could go well beyond the confines of classical computers to create powerful new materials, turbocharge the fight against climate change and completely upend cryptography.

In theory, the very nature of quantum mechanics poses a fundamental challenge for computing. To do calculations, you need to be able to measure things, and pass on the results of what you find to the next stage of the equation. But measuring something in superposition knocks it out of that state: the photon no longer appears to be in two places at once; Schrödinger's cat is either dead or alive. You need to be able to move that spinning coin around without disturbing its spin.

In fact, this is possible, thanks to another weird feature of quantum mechanics called 'entanglement'. When two electron waves interact with each other, each one leaves a mark on the other. This means that they're inextricably linked, or 'entangled', no matter how far apart they drift. Even if they're separated by billions of miles, measuring one entangled particle instantly changes the state of the other one – the wave function of both particles collapses at the same time. It's an observation which has puzzled physicists for decades. There is something linking the two particles, and it means that quantum information can be transferred from one place to another, without the underlying superposition collapsing. Entanglement solves the measurement problem. It means that you can pass information from one qubit to another without collapsing the superposition.

Deutsch's insights were of critical importance, and by 1992 people were starting to pay attention to the world of quantum computing. But the idea might have remained in the world of theory if it hadn't been for Giuseppe Castagnoli, head of IT at Elsag Bailey, a manufacturer of industrial control systems that is now part of ABB. 'At the time I was in charge of the Information Communication Technology Division of Elsag Bailey, and was personally interested in quantum computation, which was in its very early stage,' remembers Castagnoli, now 78 and still publishing papers on quantum cryptography. 'When I saw the possibility of an industrial application of quantum computation and communication, I approached the scientific community.'

'He persuaded his company that, instead of sponsoring some art exhibition, he would sponsor a series of conferences,' recalls Artur Ekert, a professor of quantum physics at the University of Oxford and an early attendee of Castagnoli's annual workshops at Villa Gualino, a hillside hotel overlooking Turin, from 1993 to 1998. Here, the young academics who are now among the most influential people in quantum computing rubbed shoulders and exchanged ideas.

In 1994, Ekert gave a talk to the International Conference on Atomic Physics in Boulder, Colorado, based on some of the ideas he'd absorbed at Villa Gualino. For the first time, he broke down quantum computation into its basic building blocks, drawing parallels with classical devices and describing the types of switches and logic gates that would be needed to build a quantum machine. Logic gates do things like combine the inputs from two bits and spit out one answer – so only displaying a 1 if both input gates are 1, for instance.

Ekert's talk marked the birth of quantum computing as an industry. 'This meeting started the whole avalanche,' he says. 'All of a sudden the computer scientists were talking about algorithms; atomic physicists saw that they could play a role. Later it started spilling over into other fields, it started accelerating, and it became the industry you see today.'

Before it could become an industry, though, scientists had to figure out how to actually build a qubit. In the 1990s, this was still an entirely theoretical construct. To make quantum computing work, scientists needed to find or create something that was small enough to adhere to the laws of quantum mechanics, but also big enough to be reliably controlled. It's a quest that has pushed our understanding of physics and material science to the limit.

2

Building the impossible

Google's quantum lab is just north of Santa Barbara, California, in a squat, beige building around the corner from a beer distributor. It doesn't look like the home of the next big breakthrough in technology – but you could probably have said the same thing about Bletchley Park in the 1940s. There are rows of messy desks, and surfboards hanging on the wall – at lunch, a group of engineers play Nintendo in a meeting room named after Richard Feynman, and there's a bed and bowl set aside for Qubit, the office dog.

The real action is in the hardware lab itself, through a set of double doors plastered with nerdy stickers featuring jokes that you'd need a PhD in quantum mechanics to understand. Inside, everything is clean, white and precise.

The hum of machinery fills the air, and there's a quiet, almost reverent level of concentration among the handful of people working in the area. This is where Google's 53-qubit Sycamore chip achieved quantum supremacy, and ushered in a new dawn for computer science.

When Artur Ekert gave his talk at Boulder in 1994, the qubit was still an entirely theoretical construct. To make quantum computers a reality, physicists had to find a way to actually build a qubit – a single switch that could be reliably flicked between one and zero, and that could also exist in a state of superposition. It needed to be something small enough to adhere to the laws of quantum mechanics, but big enough and stable enough to be reliably controlled.

Those two conditions are challenging enough. But there's a third problem that quantum engineers spend their time grappling with: interference – not from other qubits, but from the outside world. When you're working on the quantum scale, the slightest noise can nudge a qubit out of the delicate state of superposition, like a breeze blowing out a candle or toppling a spinning coin. In the industry this is called 'decoherence', and it typically happens within a fraction of a second. 'You're simultaneously trying to really well isolate the inner workings of a quantum computer and yet be able to tell it what to do and to get the answer out of it,' says Chetan Nayak, Microsoft's general manager of quantum hardware.

It's all part of a delicate balancing act. Each quantum computation is a frantic race to perform as many operations as possible in the fraction of a second before a qubit 'decoheres' out of superposition. 'The lifetime of the quantum information is super-short,' explains Jan Goetz of the Finnish start-up IQM, which is developing technology to try and increase the clock speed of quantum chips and improve their performance in this regard. 'The more complex you make the processors, the more the lifetime goes down.'

Every new control method you add in also adds more interference and noise. 'Every time we add a line into that it actually adds decoherence,' says Google's Tony

Megrant. 'We're hurting our device, but can we somehow overall end up better? The most challenging thing is how can you get a quantum system with sufficient lifetime to operate long enough that you can do meaningful things.'

That's why most of the room is taken up by six cryostats, arranged in two rows of three. These are nested metal cylinders, each painted in one of Google's corporate colours, hanging down from the ceiling and narrowing slightly from top to bottom, like a chandelier. They're designed to gradually cool a quantum chip to a temperature that's colder than outer space, and keep it completely isolated from heat, noise, vibration and electromagnetic interference. The cryostats gradually step down the temperature – each level gets progressively colder, and it takes the whole machine almost two days to get the quantum chip down to 10 millikelvin, and nearly a week to warm back up to room temperature. 'It's all about how to protect the lifetime of the system,' says Yu Chen, a quantum research scientist at Google who focuses on measuring and calibrating the systems.

Computing with lasers

Google's technology is just one of a number of different attempts to build working qubits. Artur Ekert's talk sparked research in a number of different directions – all proceeding in parallel like climbers taking different routes up a mountain. There have been dozens of different approaches dating back to the early days of quantum computing – qubits have been suspended in laser beams, trapped in diamonds and inferred from the aggregate magnetic alignment of billions of particles in a machine that works like an MRI scanner. Some routes offer a more gentle starting slope before accelerating in difficulty, while others have a steeper initial learning curve, but promise to be easier to scale up to the thousands or millions of qubits we'll eventually need to solve real-world problems.

The earliest efforts were based on ion traps, a technology that grew out of well-established work on atomic clocks, which were developed in the mid-twentieth century to provide supremely accurate timekeeping by tapping into the internal metronome of an atom. An ion is an atom with a positive or negative charge (rather than a neutral one). In trapped-ion quantum computing, qubits are formed from individual ions which are held in tiny wells, with pulses of lights used to nudge them between different states, and stop them jiggling around, like a cruise ship being held in place by tug boats.[1] In May 1995, Peter Zoller and Ignacio Cirac from the University of Innsbruck in Austria – who were also part of the nascent quantum community that met annually in Turin – published a paper[2] describing how ions could be used as qubits for simple operations, and how the states of 1, 0 and superposition could be encoded in the rocking motion of the ion, or the energy level or 'spin' of one of the electrons that orbits it.

Ekert had described the need to build a particular type of quantum logic gate known as a CNOT gate – a two-bit gate where the second bit only flipped from

1 to 0 if the first bit was in a certain state. In classical computers, which consist of a complex network of logic gates composed of individual bits, you can make any type of circuit from what are known as NOR and NAND gates. CNOT gates are the quantum equivalent. If they could be achieved, Ekert said, it meant that computer scientists would have everything they needed to start building quantum circuits.

In 1995, just a year later, a team at the National Institute of Standards and Technology (NIST) at Boulder was able to build a working CNOT gate using a single ion of the element beryllium. A laser pulse would change the spin of the orbiting electron from up to down (or 1 to 0), but only if the ion was vibrating in a certain way (which corresponded to 1 rather than 0). They'd created a working two-qubit quantum gate – but they'd need many more than that to build a working quantum computer.

Ion traps have perhaps the gentlest gradient of all the routes up the quantum mountain, because they're not reliant on any new technologies being developed. 'The physics is done,' says Peter Chapman, president and CEO of Baltimore-based, Amazon-backed IonQ, which is attempting to commercialise a trapped-ion quantum computer. 'I like to joke that IonQ computers are largely built and delivered in parts from Amazon – it's pretty much off the shelf.'

Using ions has cons as well as pros. On the plus side, ions don't have to be made – they simply exist in nature. 'We don't have a manufacturing problem,' Chapman says. 'Mother Nature manufactures atoms.' That brings huge advantages in terms of the amount of shielding required – trapped ions are much less likely to get knocked out of superposition by environmental interference.

On the minus side, because ions are so small, trapped-ion quantum computing is harder – some say impossible – to scale to the level required for a useful quantum computer, which would need hundreds or thousands of qubits. Chapman argues that this could be achieved by creating separate, smaller quantum devices and shuttling information between them using light.

Another early approach to quantum computing offered a quite different solution to the problem of decoherence. Instead of trying to isolate qubits from the environment, it simply accepted that some will inevitably decohere, and solved the problem by sheer force of numbers.

In 2001, IBM researchers in San Jose, California, led by Isaac Chung were able to create a working quantum computer using a small amount of liquid and magnets. They used a molecule containing five fluorine atoms and two carbon atoms. Each of the seven atoms in this molecule has its own spin state, so effectively the molecule could operate as a seven-qubit quantum computer, if you could reliably control it.

That is impossible, but by collecting together trillions of these molecules in a liquid, the researchers were able to control them en masse, and create largely the same effect. They used a nuclear magnetic resonance machine (akin to the MRI scanner in a hospital) to monitor the liquid, while hitting it with controlled electromagnetic pulses that flipped certain molecules in the sample into the desired state. Even if only a small proportion actually entered this state, it didn't matter, because their combined signal was still strong enough to stand out against the random background noise of the rest of the sample. 'In effect, the "readout" from the computer averaged over all the molecules,' explains John Gribbin in *Computing with Quantum Cats*,[3] 'with the huge number of right answers effectively swamping the much smaller number of errors introduced by decoherence and other difficulties.'

But this approach has largely fallen by the wayside, along with others ranging from quantum dots to computers made of diamond. Ion traps, too, are largely out of favour, despite their early promise (although some companies, including IonQ, are still pursuing them). Today, therefore, the major players in the field have largely coalesced around one group of technologies – superconducting qubits.

The cold path to supremacy

Most PhD students are happy simply to finish their thesis. Brian Josephson's final project helped him win a share of the Nobel Prize.

In 1962, the 22-year-old Cambridge student was studying superconductivity – a phenomenon where the electrical resistance of some materials drops to zero when they're cooled below a certain temperature. (Resistance measures how easily a current can flow through a material – copper has low resistance, rubber high; the higher the resistance, the more voltage needed to keep a current flowing.) In the course of his research, Josephson discovered that, in accordance with the laws of quantum physics, if you joined two superconductors together through a weak link of another material, you could create a current that flowed through them forever without any further voltage being applied. These structures, which are now known as Josephson junctions, have a wide range of applications in electronics and computing.

Although they are quantum devices, you don't need a microscope to see them – some Josephson junctions are as big as a wedding ring, but they're now made small enough to fit on a silicon chip. They also have another useful property called non-linearity, which enables them to be restricted to just two energy states – representing 1 and 0 – regardless of how much energy is put into them. They can, writes Gribbin, 'be used as fast, ultra-sensitive switches which can be turned on and off using light'.[4]

Superconducting qubits, composed of these Josephson junctions, offer a technology that promises to be easier to scale and miniaturise than ion traps, as it meshes more neatly with the silicon-based architecture inside almost every classical computer on the planet. What started out as a hedge position at Google, which had initially focused its efforts on other approaches, is now the frontrunner for both the search giant and IBM, its major quantum rival.

'Every approach has positive and negative aspects,' says Sergio Boixo, who works on quantum theory at Google, and who designed the task that proved quantum supremacy. 'This approach – superconducting qubits – has always been looked at as being the closest analogue to the classical integrated circuit that powers our lives. Once we get past certain shortcomings that come along with this package, we can scale up just like classical computing. We're going to get all of those benefits and we just have to overcome the negatives.' 'Superconducting qubits are big enough that you can control them,' adds Megrant. 'Other systems have lower intrinsic errors, but if they're too small you can't get the circuitry to control them properly.'

Both Google and IBM use microwave pulses to control their qubits, and alter their relative probability of being in the 0 or 1 state. But their approaches do differ slightly. 'Tiny fabrication defects mean that no two qubits respond to pulses of exactly the same frequency,' explains Gideon Lichfield in an article published in

MIT Technology Review.[5] 'There are two solutions to this: vary the frequency of the pulses to find each qubit's sweet spot, like jiggling a badly cut key in a lock until it opens; or use magnetic fields to "tune" each qubit to the right frequency.'

Google uses the second approach – and by passing a current through the system researchers can modify the thresholds for each state and the strengths of the connection between qubits, enabling them to become entangled. Its qubits are faster and more precise, but perhaps not as reliable in the long term as IBM's simpler, more stable approach of varying the pulse frequency.

Solving this technical challenge has proved to be only half the problem. The phenomena that superconducting qubits rely on only emerge at incredibly low temperatures, which is just one of the reasons they are so difficult to get right. 'We've front-loaded most of our problems in this field,' Megrant says. 'All of the problems show up on day one when you try to make a single qubit. You have to work very hard to have it perform well.'

Google's 53-qubit Sycamore chip sits at the bottom of one of the huge cryostats in the lab, where its temperature is cryogenically maintained. Like its predecessor Bristlecone, Sycamore was manufactured at the University of California, Santa Barbara, sandwiched together like an Oreo to create the fragile Josephson junction. Under the microscope, each qubit looks like a tiny, silvery plus sign. Thin lines lead out to the edge of the chip: eventually, they connect up to the tangle of blue wires that carry and amplify the faint signal from the qubit to one of the racks of machines surrounding each cryostat.

It takes up to two weeks to wire up one of the machines. To increase the number of qubits, Google will need to find a new wiring solution that takes up less space, or find a way of controlling the qubit from inside the cryostat. 'A lot of things will just break if you try to cool down to 10 millikelvin,' says Megrant. Both Microsoft and Google are now working on building classical chips that can operate at lower temperatures in order to control the qubits without adding interference.

Harry Potter and the missing Majorana

Over the last ten years, there has been an escalating race in the number of qubits being claimed by different companies. In 2016, Google simulated a hydrogen molecule with a 9-bit quantum computer. In 2017, Intel reached 17 qubits, and IBM built a 50-qubit chip that could maintain its quantum state for 50 microseconds. In 2018, Google unveiled Bristlecone, its 72-qubit processor, and, in 2019, IBM launched its first commercial quantum computer – the 20-qubit IBM Q System One, to great media fanfare.

D-Wave, a Canada-based company, has always been an outlier. It has been selling commercial quantum computers since the late 1990s, and claims to have several thousand 'annealing qubits' in its devices, but these are based on a different technology that's only useful for certain types of problems. IonQ's Peter Chapman likens it to the difference between a graphics calculator and a computer.

Rob Young, director of Lancaster University's Quantum Technology Centre, accuses some companies of a lack of credibility in the way they've announced these developments. 'There's a real question of how you translate your findings without being over-sensational,' he says.

It's becoming clear that the number of qubits isn't nearly as important as what Heike Riel, head of the science and technology department at IBM Research Europe, calls 'quantum volume' – how much useful computation you can do before your qubits decohere. Quantum volume is a combination of the number of qubits, the way those qubits are wired up, and how accurate and reliable the qubits are. 'The number of qubits is of course important, but it's not everything,' Riel says. 'Quantum volume tells you how much useful computation you can do with a device before the error will mask your result.'

Even with all the technology Google employs to shield its qubits from interference, the error rate is still astonishingly high. Qubits routinely flip into the wrong state, or decohere before they're supposed to. It's possible to correct for those errors, but to do it, you need more qubits – and more qubits to correct for those qubits.

There's also an important distinction to be drawn between the number of physical qubits on a quantum chip, and the number of logical qubits that those physical qubits enable you to operate with. Google's Sycamore chip may have 53 physical qubits, for instance, but because of the need to use a number of those qubits for error correction, it's not technically equivalent to a 53-qubit quantum computer. 'If you want hundreds of logical qubits you need tens of thousands of physical qubits,' says Peter Shor, a hugely influential quantum theorist, 'and we're very far away from that.'

With current error rates, you would need thousands or millions of qubits to run algorithms that might be useful in the real world. That's why John Preskill, the physicist who coined the term 'quantum supremacy', has dubbed this era 'noisy intermediate scale quantum' (NISQ), in recognition of the fact that we're a long way off practical devices.

It's also why Microsoft is convinced that super-conducting qubits are a dead end. 'We do not see a line of sight there to commercial-scale quantum computers that could solve today's unsolvable problems,' says Chetan Nayak. Instead, at Microsoft's sprawling headquarters in Redmond, Washington (so big that the quickest way between meetings is by Uber), researchers are testing a cryostat that looks very similar to Google's, but which will – if things go to plan – host a very different type of quantum processor. If Google's ascent up the quantum mountain is steep, Microsoft's is potentially impossible. Instead of superconducting qubits, it's trying to harness a different type of qubit known as a 'topological qubit'. The only problem is that topological qubits may not actually exist. 'Maybe we're on a marathon instead of a sprint,' says Krysta Svore, Microsoft's general manager for quantum software.

Topological qubits, if they can be created, offer a more robust alternative to superconducting qubits that are harder to knock out of superposition. As a result, you'd need ten times fewer qubits. They're qubits based on a theoretical particle called a Majorana particle, which encodes the state of the qubit in several places at once. Nayak explains it using a Harry Potter analogy. 'The main villain of the story, Voldemort, splits his soul into seven pieces called Horcruxes, and spreads out those Horcruxes so he can't be killed,' he says. 'What we're doing with our topological qubit is spreading our qubit out over six Majoranas. Those are our Horcruxes. By doing something to just one or another of them locally, you actually can't kill off Voldemort. Our qubit is still going to be there.'

The only problem is that scientists still aren't entirely sure that Majorana particles actually exist. They've been theorised about since the 1930s, but the experimental evidence isn't watertight. Still, speaking in January 2020, Nayak and Svore were confident. 'We're not hunting in the dark for this and hoping to find this,' said Nayak. 'We're being guided by simulations.'

Although superconducting qubits seem to have the upper hand at present, it's still unclear which technology will support the quantum computers of the future. 'We're not in the days of AMD vs Intel. We're in the days of vacuum tubes versus little mechanical gates,' says Whurley. Different technologies will have breakthroughs, while others stagnate, and it could be decades before a clear path emerges. 'They'll go back and forth, and maybe eventually at some point down the line we'll have our dream of a millions-of-qubits machine and a general-purpose quantum computer.'

As a case in point, recent developments in trapped-ion computing could give it the edge for developing quantum devices with thousands or millions of qubits. In June 2020, Universal Quantum – a spin-out from the University of Sussex – announced that it had picked up £3.6 million of funding for a new form of trapped-ion computing. Its approach seems to combine the best bits of both Google and IBM's superconducting approach, and the ion trap method used by IonQ.

Winfried Hensinger, co-founder and chief scientist at Universal Quantum, points out that the big limiting factor for Google's device isn't the quantum chip itself, but the cooling system, which would need to grow bigger and bigger to chill down a larger area as the number of qubits increased. Because Universal Quantum uses ion trap technology, such extreme cooling isn't necessary – and it has found a clever way of getting around the problem of scalability. Instead of using laser beams – to support millions of qubits in a full-scale quantum device would require millions of them – it's using electric fields to control the qubit. Microwaves are used to move the qubit between energy states – but, rather than trying to accurately hit individual qubits with microwave pulses, UQ's technology instead uses electric fields to nudge the qubits into a state where they're receptive to global microwave pulses. It's not dissimilar to the way Google uses microwave pulses to tune its superconducting qubits.

The company is working on creating modules that can be connected together to scale up quickly: to send messages from module to module, an ion is coerced into jumping across a tiny gap between modules, like neurotransmitters jumping between synapses in the brain.

Whatever the way forward, the last 40 years of theorising and 25 years of cutting-edge hardware development have brought the field to a crucially important point. Quantum supremacy means that the algorithms being developed can be tested and improved – and that quantum computing can begin to have a small real-world impact on everything from medicine to traffic control while we wait for the hardware to catch up. 'Quantum supremacy is a signal for us to say we've entered the era of NISQ,' says Tony Megrant. 'Now you have this large-enough system, and instead of using your laptop you can just go and play.'

3
Exponential power

In May 2000, the Clay Mathematics Institute in Peterborough, New Hampshire, established a set of seven seemingly intractable mathematical problems, and offered a $1 million prize for anyone who could solve them. To date, only one of these Millennium Prize Problems – the Poincaré conjecture – has been successfully cracked, by the elusive Russian mathematician Grigori Perelman, who declined the prize money and then retired from the field for good.

Arguably the most important of all of the challenges set by the institute is the P versus NP problem. P refers to all the mathematical problems which can be easily solved by computers in 'polynomial time' – a slightly tricky concept for non-mathematicians, but which basically means anything that a supercomputer like Summit could handle in a reasonable amount of time. NP problems, on the other hand, are ones which aren't easily solvable in a reasonable amount of time, but where it's easy to check whether you've got the right solution if you're presented with a potential answer.

A classic example of an NP problem is factoring – breaking down a large number into its smallest possible prime factors. So, for instance, the prime factors of 35 are 7 and 5 – two numbers that you can multiply together to make 35, but which aren't divisible by any other numbers themselves. Computationally, figuring out prime factors is quite difficult, because no real patterns seem to emerge, so you have to manually rule out first all the multiples of 2, then the multiples of 3, and so on until you're left with only the primes. For small numbers, that's fine, but for larger ones the challenge grows exponentially. But it's always easy to check that you've got the right answer – simply multiply the primes together and see if the result matches your original number.

The debate mathematicians have been having for years is whether P equals NP, or not. The $1 million prize is for someone who can definitely prove that every problem that's easy to verify is easy to solve, or the opposite. If P does equal NP, then it means that a raft of seemingly impossible problems are solvable by computers, but we just haven't found the right algorithm yet. If P doesn't equal NP, then it means that there are certain computational challenges that may always remain unresolvable and beyond our reach. Part of the allure of quantum computing is that it drags some NP problems closer to being solvable in a reasonable amount of time, provided that we can find the right kind of algorithm.

One of the key misunderstandings about quantum computers is that people think of them as simply a faster type of supercomputer – a new technology that we can apply to all the problems we have today and get answers thousands or millions of times faster. Sadly, that isn't the case. 'The types of problem where quantum computers can have an advantage are NP problems that have more "structure" than a general NP problem,' says Andrea Rocchetto, a quantum computing researcher at the University of Texas at Austin: 'something that you can exploit to reduce the number of computational steps you need to solve the problem.'

Factoring, Rocchetto says, is in the boundary between problems that have so much structure that it's easy to find an efficient solution (P problems) and problems where there's hardly any structure for even a quantum computer to get its teeth into. 'Quantum computers need structure,' he says. 'Without structure there is no magic – it's not some kind of black box that, whatever problem you put into it, it will come out with an answer.' The onus is on mathematicians and computer scientists to find clever algorithms that can detect and exploit the structure of NP problems – to bring them within the reach of quantum computers. In 1994, a researcher at Bell Labs did just that – and his discovery could have huge implications for quantum computing, cryptography and much, much more.

The Q factor

Peter Shor is a mathematician, an amateur poet and the creator of one of the most influential algorithms in history. In 1994, Shor was working at Bell Labs – the famed research and development wing of the telecoms company – where he attended a couple of talks on quantum encryption. He had studied quantum physics at university, and was intrigued by the potential applications of quantum computing, which – as described earlier – arise from the curious property of quantum interference, where the different potential paths that a photon could take interfere with one another to create the end result. Although quantum computers were still years away from becoming a physical reality, Shor and others started thinking about the algorithms that would run on them, and what they could do.

In its simplest form, an algorithm is simply a set of instructions or rules to follow in problem-solving operations, but quantum algorithms have to be designed in accordance with the unique properties of quantum mechanics. 'Quantum computers use interference in their fundamental algorithms,' Shor explains. 'You can think of the computation going through all sorts of different paths – and each path has a corresponding phase. If you can somehow arrange the computation so that all the correct answers have the same phase, the probability of seeing a correct answer gets increased.'

Shor's algorithm applies that insight to create a method for factoring large numbers. It uses a series of mathematical tricks to turn the number to be factored into a 'wave' of smaller ones that repeat in some fixed sequence. He realised that the rhythm and frequency of this wave – known as its period – is related to the factors of the original number. Shor draws an analogy with a diffraction grating, a physical object that splits light into different wavelengths like a prism: a beam of white light goes in one end, and a rainbow emerges from the other. All the light of a certain wavelength gets amplified at one point in space, and the all the light of another gets amplified at a different point. Shor's algorithm acts like a mathematical prism: large numbers go in one end, and the factors come out of the other.

Shor's method is laborious and unwieldy for classical computers but, crucially, it is structured in such a way that the calculations involved can be performed simultaneously on a quantum computer. 'This was the first provable case of a problem where a classical computer needs to expand exponential resources, and a quantum computer doesn't,' says Rocchetto. Shor's algorithm can factor large numbers exponentially quicker than classical computers – the bigger the number, the more of an advantage it provides. It caused shockwaves across the quantum community, and helped kickstart the field in a big way because of its implications for cybersecurity, which we'll cover in detail in the next chapter. 'This is what ignited a lot of interest in the field – both on the theoretical side and also on the commercial and defence side,' Rocchetto says. 'It was a breakthrough for both communities.'

Similarly powerful breakthroughs have proved harder to find, however. Most other quantum algorithms that have been developed so far only offer a more modest quadratic speed-up instead of the exponential increase provided by Shor's algorithm. 'The quadratic speed-up – where we improve the run time of the classical algorithm, but not enough to make it an easy problem, can be extremely relevant in real-world scenarios,' says Rocchetto. 'These quadratic speed-ups are harder to detect – it's a matter of trying in practice – but they can still be extremely significant. They could help save companies immense amounts of money.'

In 1996, another Bell Labs researcher devised an algorithm that could help explain why Google in particular is pumping so much money into building a quantum computer. Lov Grover demonstrated that quantum computers could be used to massively speed up how quickly an unordered database could be searched. If you give a classical computer the phone book, and ask it to find a particular number, it has to check each and every entry in turn until it finds the right one. You can speed up the process by throwing multiple processors at the problem – start one going from the top of the list and one from the bottom, for instance – but the average time required still grows rapidly with the size of the list to be searched.

Grover's algorithm describes a method for searching a database using the power of quantum interference. By encoding each of the items in the list in superposition, their waves can be manipulated so that the wrong answers cancel one another out, and the right answers reinforce one another. Again, the method is too complex to describe in detail here, but the implications are huge. Over multiple steps of processing, the correct answer simply rises to the top – as if all the other numbers in the phonebook had slowly faded away. Grover showed that while a classical computer would have to look through 500,000 items on average to find the right one in a list a million entries long, a quantum computer running his algorithm would only need to search a thousand. It provides a quadratic speed-up over classical devices. A quantum device only needs to look through the square root of the number of items – and for a million items you'd only need 20 qubits.

Together, Shor and Grover equipped quantum computers with two powerful weapons that promised to transform everything from cryptography to finance. In theory, anyway. But in the real world – where equations and elegant algorithms crash into reality – things are a lot more complicated.

Margins of error

Shor's and Grover's algorithms were designed for a perfect quantum computer. But when they were written in the mid-1990s such a thing didn't exist, and it still doesn't. Despite claims of quantum supremacy, we're still in the 'NISQ' era, which means that the best devices are still noisy and error-prone – their qubits still flip into the wrong state or slide out of superposition. Even the best quantum computers – chilled to near-impossible temperatures and isolated behind shields – still have error rates that are too high. According to a 2019 talk[1] by John Preskill, the probability of error per two-qubit gate in a quantum system, using the best hardware available at the time, is about 0.1 per cent. Similarly, the probability of error per measurement is around 1 per cent, which is way too high for anything useful. 'Theory is well ahead of experiment,' says Rob Young. 'The really big, important problem is that the vast majority of algorithms that are being considered today are so far ahead of where the performance metrics of the real quantum systems are, that you don't know if they are ever going to be useful.'

For a long time, many thought that the problem of error correction was insurmountable – a fatal flaw in quantum computing. Some researchers still believe this. 'My analysis shows that noisy quantum computers with a few dozen qubits deliver such primitive computational power,' the Yale professor Gil Kalai told *WIRED* in 2019, 'that it will simply not be possible to use them as the building blocks we need to build quantum computers on a wider scale.'[2]

Errors are a problem for classical computers too, but there are well-established systems in place to identify and correct them – based on sending several copies of the same message and comparing them for differences, or sending each bit a set number of times, so that even if one or two get randomly flipped the overall message is still clear, or using what are known as parity bits to check that a message has been correctly received.

That doesn't work for quantum computers, because each of those systems involves measuring the bits – which knocks them out of superposition and kills the benefits. It is possible to mitigate some of the error simply by repeating each computation hundreds or thousands of times, which is what Google's researchers did during their quantum supremacy experiment – repeat measurements help to separate the signal from the noise. But mitigating noise doesn't solve the problem, particularly when you try to scale that up to larger devices with more qubits.

However, clever work by Shor and others proved that quantum error correction is possible, if you have enough qubits. 'To protect against multiple errors, you would need to surround each qubit with dozens of redundant qubits,' explains George Johnson in his book *A Shortcut Through Time*. 'And then, when an error was found, you would have to worry about more errors creeping into the correction process itself. Guarding against that would require still more redundancy.'

These error-correction algorithms are designed in such a way as to measure the error without affecting the computation – they use 'parity bits' that aren't part of the calculation, but are affected by it if something goes wrong. A similar system is used for credit card numbers – the first 15 digits of the long number on the front of the card are determined by your bank and card issuer, but the final digit is generated by feeding the first 15 digits into a special algorithm. This allows the entity processing someone's card details to check for errors without knowing the original card number – but requires extra resources (in this case, extra digits in the card number).

'The problem with error correction is that if you want to correct errors and you do not have very accurate quantum gates, it takes an enormous amount of overhead,' says Shor. 'It's going to multiply the number of qubits and the time you need to run the computer by thousands or tens of thousands.' While on paper, Shor's algorithm only needs a few thousand qubits, in practice you'd actually need a lot more to handle error correction when factoring large numbers – maybe a million or more physical qubits, according to Boixo. 'In terms of practical application, you would definitely need a fault-tolerant quantum computer or a significant advancement in the algorithm itself.' Others are working on fault-tolerant algorithms, which would be naturally resistant to errors because of the way they're written. But even those will require vast improvements in the underlying hardware. Despite Google's achievement of quantum supremacy, we're still a long way off practical quantum computers in the NISQ era.

But that hasn't stopped companies ploughing ahead, and trying to deploy some of the quantum computing techniques they've learned to everything from reducing traffic jams to diagnosing cancer.

Traffic unjammed

Seattle is a city that is being devoured by big tech. Between Microsoft's home in Redmond and the voracious appetite of Amazon, the city is a mess of cranes and construction works, with numerous road closures adding to the traffic problems caused by its harbour setting and inclement weather. An incident on one of the city's many bridges can quickly lead to long traffic jams.

Mapping apps, which are designed to reroute drivers when there are potential delays, can actually end up making the problem worse. They're selfish. When you request a route, Google Maps will give you the quickest route for you at that moment, without taking into account how your journey might delay the journeys of other users, or how hundreds of people using the same section of road will lead to bottlenecks. A more balanced routing system would consider each of the route requests together, and suggest routes that helped to minimise bottlenecks and keep traffic flowing faster. But there's a practical barrier: a system like that would require vast amounts of computational power. This is what's known as an optimisation problem. There are thousands of different types, from figuring out the best order for a delivery driver to make his stops, to figuring out how many packages will fit in the back of his truck before you send it on its way. Anything where you need to maximise efficiency or minimise costs is an optimisation problem, and right now they're largely tackled by trial and error.

Most optimisation problems, including the famous travelling salesman problem (see p. 11), don't have the kind of underlying structure that would allow quantum computers to solve them exponentially quicker than classical computers. But quantum computers could certainly solve them more quickly, according to Christopher Savoie of Zapata Computing, and come up with considerably better answers. And in the meantime, even though we still live in a pre-quantum computer era, the algorithms that have been derived to run on them can be used to solve smaller optimisation problems on existing, classical hardware.

In 2018, for instance, Microsoft's quantum researchers teamed up with Ford on a project aimed at improving traffic flow in Seattle. They created a virtual model of traffic in the city, and ran a simulation with more than 5,000 vehicles simultaneously requesting one of ten different routes each. According to Microsoft, using quantum-inspired algorithms instead of the selfish routing used by current systems resulted in a 73 per cent reduction in congestion, an 8 per cent drop in commuting time, and would save more than 55,000 hours a year for the drivers of these vehicles if deployed in the real world. 'Optimisation is the most fruitful area for exploration, because there are these complex problems that pop up in every industry,' says Ben

Porter, director of business development for Microsoft's quantum operations. 'It doesn't matter whether you're talking automotive, aerospace, utilities – there are some rich areas for us to explore.'

Financial services are another potentially lucrative area where quantum computers could have a big impact in future. The 2008 financial crash was caused, in part, by the inability of banks and regulators to correctly analyse risk in a complex system. Researchers working with IBM have been testing quantum algorithms to see if they might be better than classical ones at running a Monte Carlo simulation, a common way of analysing risk that often takes days to run through millions of simulations of a particular scenario. 'A quantum computer can provide a quadratic speed-up – instead of many million scenarios, we only require a few thousands to achieve the same accuracy,' says IBM mathematician Stefan Woerner.[3] That's enough to take the running time for a Monte Carlo simulation from something that needs to be done overnight to something that can happen in close to real time – you can imagine the implications for stock market traders.

But perhaps one of the most exciting applications of quantum computing could be in the field of machine learning. For decades, algorithms for classical computers were written by hand – painstakingly crafted by coders, who were like chefs writing down detailed recipes. But as computing power got cheaper, artificial intelligence and machine learning came to the fore. Now, the algorithms behind everything from facial recognition to online translation are more likely to be created by training a general-purpose program on a vast set of data. These technologies are hugely powerful. They can, for instance, diagnose lung cancer from scans more successfully than human experts. But they're only as good as the data you feed them on. If you don't have good enough data, or your underlying data is biased, you end up with flawed, biased algorithms.

Quantum computing offers the possibility of creating data where none actually exists in the real world, through a process known as generative modelling. It's a process that's already being carried out on classical computers, but quantum devices could do it faster and at a larger scale. 'If we have a sample of a hundred things, we can use generative modelling to create things that are similar,' explains Savoie. The additional power of quantum computers could be used to extrapolate from limited data sets, and feed machine-learning algorithms with data, even when we don't have it. 'Enhancing this allows us to do things with scant data – whether that's looking for rare lung cancer in MRIs, or in facial recognition, where you have a lot of pictures of the side of a face but not the front of a face,' says Savoie. It is, he says, like creating deep fakes that are as good as the real thing.

As deep fakes have demonstrated, tools like AI and machine learning can be hugely beneficial, or tremendously disruptive, depending on whose hands they're in. Quantum computers are likely to have the same impact. If they work, they will undoubtedly bring benefits to the worlds of biology, chemistry and physics. But there are risks to such powerful machines being concentrated in the hands of a select few large companies or national governments. Some are worried that quantum computers could also upend the security systems that protect everything from banking systems to military secrets.

4
Cracking the code

In June 2013, the American whistleblower Edward Snowden released thousands of classified documents to the media relating to the practices of the US National Security Agency (NSA). The documents created uproar in the press and shockwaves in global politics, as the extent of the NSA's surveillance on its own citizens and those of other countries came to light. Snowden was forced into exile.

The famous incident had another facet. It was also a pivotal moment in the global battle to gain the upper hand in quantum technologies. While security agencies stockpile vast amounts of data in the hope of one day soon having a computer that can decode it, researchers are scrambling to develop quantum-secure communication and encryption methods.

According to analysis by the Washington think-tank Center for a New American Security (CNAS),[1] Snowden's revelations spooked the Chinese government so much that it began searching for new, home-grown solutions for cybersecurity that would protect it from the NSA's prying eyes. 'Chinese leaders seem to hope that quantum networks can serve as a shield that ensures the "absolute security" of critical communications,' write the report's authors, Elsa Kania and John Costello.

The security protocols that many nations rely on could soon be under threat because of quantum computers, and because of Peter Shor in particular. When he wrote his factoring algorithm in 1994, it immediately attracted attention from the defence industry, because it threatened to break the underlying encryption technology that supports much of our cybersecurity infrastructure.

All manner of sensitive data, from military documents to credit card numbers, is protected using codes that rely on the difficulty of factoring large numbers. This method, known as RSA encryption after its creators Ronald Rivest, Adi Shamir and Leonard Adleman, is also known as public-key cryptography. Before RSA, if you wanted to send a coded message, you'd take the text and then pass it through a series of well-defined steps. These could be something as simple as transposing the letters, so that A becomes B, B becomes C and so on, or something more complicated. One difficult-to-crack method involves turning a string of text into a long string of digits, and then multiplying or adding a random number to it. Only someone who knows this random number, known as the 'key', can easily decrypt and read the message's contents. The challenge is getting the key to the recipient without it also being intercepted – in the past, banks employed couriers with locked briefcases to distribute new keys.

RSA provides a practical method for public-key cryptography, using so-called asymmetric encryption. In public-key cryptography, the instructions for encrypting a message are publicly available, but the information on how to decode that message is kept hidden. It took years for scientists to come up with a way of actually implementing it – but they eventually alighted on a solution in factoring. An individual can create a public key by multiplying two large random prime numbers together. The encoding algorithm on the sender's device then uses the recipient's public key to encrypt the message (for instance, by converting the text into binary code and then adding it to the number, although real-world implementations have many more steps).

So, when you send a WhatsApp message, for instance (the messaging platform uses end-to-end encryption), your phone will first check the recipient's public key, use that to encrypt your message, and then send the encrypted message to the other person's phone, which will use the corresponding private key to decrypt it. Decoding the message requires knowing the original prime numbers that were used to create the public key, and those never leave the recipient's device.

RSA encryption is virtually unbreakable, as long as it remains difficult to break large numbers down into their primes. But Shor's algorithm has made that theoretically possible. In December 2018, a report[2] by the US National Academies of Sciences, Engineering and Medicine (NAS) estimated that a quantum computer with 2,300 logical qubits could crack a 1,024-bit implementation of RSA encryption in less than 24 hours, using Shor's algorithm. Other staples of cryptography, such as AES-GCM, are potentially vulnerable to Grover's algorithm, which can more efficiently search for the correct key from all the possibilities – although again, you'd need a very powerful quantum device to do it.

When Shor's and Grover's algorithms were written in the mid-1990s, the prospect of a quantum computer good enough to run them was a distant possibility. But as well as fuelling funding for research and work into how to build such devices, their discovery also provided enough impetus to kickstart a whole new field of cybersecurity known as post-quantum cryptography.

There are a number of ways to make encryption algorithms more resistant to quantum attacks. The simplest is to just make the keys harder to break by making them longer – doubling the size of a key squares the number of permutations Grover's algorithm has to search through to find the correct one. The NAS report suggests that quadrupling the length of a 1,024-bit RSA means you'd need four times as many qubits and 64 times longer to break it. But quantum computers are developing at a rapid pace – so this approach may only buy a little bit of time. So, in 2016, the US National Institute of Standards and Technology (NIST) launched an eight-year competition[3] aimed at finding quantum-proof successors to the likes of RSA. It's thrown up dozens of potential candidates with names like Lizard, Frodo and Falcon, taking a vast array of approaches ranging from lattice-based cryptography to supersingular isogeny key exchange. Generally, it's about finding new forms of encryption that don't have the kind of underlying structure quantum computers can take advantage of – which are still exponentially difficult, even for devices with thousands or millions of qubits. 'We will have to transition to cryptographic standards that are quantum-resistant,' says Andrea Rocchetto. 'It will be transformative in this sense.'

NIST is aiming to have published draft standards for a new encryption algorithm by 2024, and it's widely expected that companies will begin to roll it out in place of RSA and other vulnerable cryptography in software soon afterwards. That won't help secure credit card numbers, passwords or government secrets which may have already been stockpiled in the expectation of being broken in future. But by the time a quantum computer good enough to run Shor's algorithm against RSA encryption actually gets built, there may be nothing new left for it to crack.

Quantum internet

In August 2016, China sent the world's first quantum satellite into space from a launch pad in the Gobi Desert. Micius, which circles the earth at an altitude of 500 kilometres, is a powerful signal of intent – a starting gun for the technological race that could define the next century. Although it remains to be seen whether quantum computers will definitely be able to break new forms of encryption algorithm, scientists aren't taking a chance. With Micius, Chinese researchers are attempting to use a different type of quantum technology to develop new forms of secure communications that would be completely unbreakable.

Micius is being used for quantum key distribution, working on the principle that even an all-powerful quantum computer can't break a key it can't get access to in the first place. It's the latest in a long line of research that involves transmitting keys from sender to receiver using photons in a state of quantum superposition, so that it's impossible to read them without changing what they say. If an attacker tries to intercept, the superposition will collapse into either 1 or 0 – leaving a telltale sign of tampering. With quantum key distribution, the message itself would still be transmitted using normal channels – it's only the key that would be communicated using quantum technology.

In theory, this technology could underpin a global network of completely secure communication channels – a quantum internet of uncrackable messages, and a safe haven for governments fearful of Snowden-like leaks (or at least, for governments with enough money to throw at the problem). However, quantum communications face a problem: photons easily get absorbed or deflected by objects in the environment, which means that quantum keys can only be transmitted short distances without extra help. You can't easily ramp up the power of the signal, because a photon is the smallest possible unit of light – adding more would risk the signal being intercepted by an attacker siphoning off photons using mirrors without you noticing. Traditional communications networks use repeaters at stages along the route to boost the signal by copying it and retransmitting it, but again that doesn't work for quantum key distribution, because copying the message requires measuring it, which knocks photons out of superposition. Instead, rather than trying to pass on the signal while it's still in superposition, it's actually decrypted at each stage before being re-encoded into a new quantum state for the next leg of the journey.

However, this in turn opens up the seemingly unbreakable system to eavesdropping at the point where the message is unscrambled and re-encrypted. Researchers have been working to develop 'quantum repeaters', which would allow the message to remain in superposition while still amplifying it. This technology has been demonstrated in theory, but working prototypes have proved more difficult to get right. It's also important to note that, just because the message itself is being sent via quantum mechanical means, it doesn't necessarily mean the entire system is unbreakable.

Charles Bennett, the IBM researcher whose work was influential in kickstarting the field of quantum cryptography and communications, pointed out a flaw in one of the early physical implementations of quantum key distribution. The cells used to generate the photons in that experiment ran off a power supply that created a faint hum, and that noise changed in volume depending on the voltage being applied. 'It's hard for a cryptosystem to be totally secure: you have to be aware of all sorts of possible attacks,' he told Julian Brown in *The Quest for the Quantum Computer*. 'So although you wouldn't be able to eavesdrop on the photons, you could just listen to the hum to find out what data were going through the system.'

Those potential flaws haven't stopped countries, China in particular, making rapid progress on quantum communication. In 2017, it completed a 2,000-kilometre quantum link between Shanghai and Beijing, with 32 stops en route for the signal to be boosted. It's designed for the secure transmission of government, finance and military information.

But for truly international quantum networks to be built, a new approach may be needed – and that's where Micius comes in. Instead of transmitting photons through fibre-optic cables, the satellite beams them through the open air – between the satellite and a ground station, and then to another ground station. This opens up the possibility of quantum communication over greater distances, although until recently it was limited to transmitting at night due to the excessive interference during daylight hours, which meant that keys had to be built up when it was dark and stored for use during the day.

In September 2017, scientists set a new record when they used the Micius satellite to hold a quantum-encrypted video call between Chinese and Austrian scientists, over a distance of 7,600 kilometres. It was the first in a number of planned launches for quantum satellites, and a significant step towards building a worldwide 'quantum internet'. 'I think we have started a worldwide quantum space race,' said the project's lead researcher Jian-Wei Pan when the satellite launched.[4]

The ultimate goal for researchers is even more ambitious. While quantum key distribution protects information from being intercepted as it travels, another method being developed means that the information never has to actually travel at all. Quantum teleportation relies on the quantum phenomenon of entanglement, where two photons are linked even if they're separated by a great distance. By creating entangled pairs of photons – one going to the sender of a message and one to the receiver – quantum teleportation means that a message can be transmitted without any data ever actually being sent. When a message is imprinted onto one of the pair of photons, by allowing it to interact with a 'memory qubit' that stores the message being sent, it instantly changes the state of the other photon. The information is effectively 'teleported' from sender to receiver. Messages sent in this way would be genuinely, completely unbreakable.

Quantum hegemony

Cybersecurity experts live in fear of 'Q-Day', or 'Y2Q' – the date when a quantum computer is developed that can break most modern cryptographic standards. If one country gets there first, it could cause problems – the CNAS report talks of 'quantum surprise', when one country develops technology that others don't even know about. It's a race that China is desperate to win. The Chinese government has made quantum the focus of a 'megaproject', and set its sights on major breakthroughs in quantum communications and quantum computing. It is reportedly investing $10 billion in building the National Laboratory for Quantum Information Sciences in Hefei. 'In the last five years, China has invested very heavily in quantum technologies,' says Rob Young, director of the Lancaster Quantum Technology Centre, and an adjunct professor at the Institute of Fundamental and Frontier Science in Chengdu. 'It has taken the lead and it has done so relatively quickly.'

The number of patents filed by Chinese companies relating to quantum computing has shot up in the last few years. In 2014, there were a similar number of patents filed in the United States and China, but by 2017 China filed almost twice as many, according to Patinformatics. China's quantum ambition has parallels with similar investments in artificial intelligence, and stems partly from a desire to position the country as the technological leader of the decades to come. 'China basically missed out on the digital revolution, and that really set them and their economy back,' says Young. 'It doesn't want to be caught napping again.' Jian-Wei Pan agrees. 'With modern information science, China has been a learner and a follower,' he says. 'Now, with quantum technology, if we try our best we can be one of the main players.' Pan has been dubbed 'the father of quantum' by the scientific journal *Nature* and, along with Snowden, is one of two key individuals behind China's advances in quantum technology.

The NSA leaks are the main reason why the bulk of China's initial progress has been not in quantum computing hardware, but instead in the field of secure quantum communications – through projects such as the Micius satellite, as well as a ground-based quantum network in the northern province of Shandong. 'In the field of quantum communications we are ahead of our colleagues over the world,' says Pan, who has said his work was given new impetus and urgency by Snowden's disclosures.

Chinese companies such as Tencent, Alibaba and Baidu have also entered the quantum race, but they're a little late to the party. 'Some years ago it was quite difficult to convince these e-commerce companies in China to invest in this kind of research,' says Pan. 'But, influenced by Google and IBM or Intel and Microsoft, all the Chinese e-commerce companies now have their own quantum technology projects.'

Chinese efforts can't yet match the performance of their US rivals in terms of raw number of qubits. However, in 2018, Chinese scientists did set a world record by linking 18 qubits together in a quantum entanglement, an interconnected state that's required for quantum computers to actually be used for calculations. That's in line with the general pattern of developments. 'There's no real evidence that the Chinese have made breakthroughs on new ways to generate qubits – that's fundamental basic science, and there's only so many ways that's going to be done,' says Tony Trippe, the managing director of Patinformatics. 'The Chinese dominance in patenting within the last four years has primarily been in the area of application.'

Where China's financial muscle could prove key is in the next phase of quantum computing. 'It's important in terms of creating a quantum environment in China,' says Artur Ekert, who proposed the theory behind Micius. 'It's not good enough to invent a telephone, for example, if it's just you who has the unit and you have no one to call. You have to have the whole infrastructure, the whole pyramid – not just a bunch of wacky physicists, but also quantum engineers, computer scientists, cryptographers, people who can sell it.' Ekert compares China's approach to NASA's Apollo project, which put a man on the Moon in the 1960s. 'It's not clear which particular quantum technology – whether it's superconducting circuits, trapped ions or something else – is going to work,' he says. 'You need to put under one roof many people who have expertise in complementary areas.'

But perhaps a comparison with Apollo – born from a fierce rivalry between the USA and the USSR – is not the right one to make. It's tempting to paint the development of quantum computing and cryptography as a zero-sum game – China vs America for the global technological crown. It's not quite like that. Jian-Wei Pan got his grounding in the technology in Europe, and Chinese researchers have been working closely with others in Austria to develop Micius and related technologies.

However, there has been a slight shift in attitude as quantum technology has moved from academia into the world of application. 'Five years ago I would have said that it was collaborative,' says Ekert, 'but in the last five years there's been a bit of a bubble'. 'A healthy degree of concern would be justified,' he adds. 'This field is just too important to have one particular region too far ahead.' For Young, the challenge is so complex and expensive that it will be hard for any one nation to steal a march on its rivals. 'I think it's very difficult these days to keep anything hidden.'

The field is fragmenting, with different research groups trying varied approaches, and countries putting their resources behind a diverse range of projects. Since 2016, when the Chinese government placed quantum at the heart of its thirteenth five-year plan, Europe and the United States have made their own investments. The European Union is putting €1 billion into its Quantum Technologies Flagship programme, which kicked into gear in 2018 with funding announced for 20 new projects. In the United States, a cross-party team has been working on legislation to inject $1.25 billion into quantum research and development. In China, they're focusing on building a multi-satellite quantum network, and creating a quantum simulator to tackle scientific problems. In the US, the big tech companies are focused on pushing up the qubit-count and bringing down the error rate on quantum computers. The UK is at the forefront of quantum algorithms. 'The really exciting thing, and the reason that the Chinese are investing in this, is that they don't know what the potential will be,' says Rob Young. 'It's clear this is going to be the next revolutionary technology, it's clear there's going to be a whole plethora of interesting devices, and they're investing in that potential.'

China's investments have certainly put it in a strong position, but it's not clear which approaches will work, and what they could lead to – the big breakthrough could come from the $10 billion quantum hub in Hefei, or from a relatively small investment elsewhere. One country could take the lead, but for quantum to become a truly revolutionary technology will require a global effort. 'It's not possible for this to be developed by a single country,' says Pan. 'We could have a race, but people need to talk and collaborate with each other.'

5

Simulating nature

The lithium-ion battery is the unsung hero of the modern world. Since it was first commercialised in the early 1990s, it has transformed the technology industry with its ability to store huge amounts of energy in a relatively small amount of space. Without lithium, there would be no iPhone or Tesla – and your laptop would be a lot bigger and heavier.

But the world is running out of this precious metal – and it could prove to be a huge bottleneck in the development of electric vehicles, and the energy storage solutions we'll need to switch to renewables. Some of the world's top scientists are engaged in a frantic race to find new battery technologies that can replace lithium-ion with something cleaner, cheaper and more plentiful. Quantum computers could be their secret weapon.

It's a similar story in agriculture, where up to 5 per cent of the world's consumption of natural gas is used in the Haber–Bosch process, a century-old method for turning nitrogen in the air into ammonia-based fertiliser for crops. It's hugely important – helping sustain about 40 per cent of the world's population – but also incredibly inefficient compared to nature's own methods. Again, quantum computers could provide the answer.

So far, researchers have been working on these problems with blunt tools. They can perform increasingly powerful simulations using classical devices, but the more complicated the reactions get, the harder they become for supercomputers to handle. This means that right now, scientists are limited to looking only at very small problems, or they are forced to sacrifice accuracy for speed.

A hydrogen atom, for instance, has one positively charged proton and one electron and is easy to simulate on a laptop – you could even work out its chemistry by hand. Helium, next step along on the periodic table, has two protons, orbited by two negatively charged electrons – but it's more challenging to simulate, because the electrons are entangled, so the state of one is linked to the state of the other, which means they all need to be calculated simultaneously.

By the time you get to thulium – which has 69 orbiting electrons, all entangled with each other – you're far beyond the capability of classical computers. If you wrote down one of each of the possible states of thulium per second it would take 20 trillion years – more than a thousand times the age of the universe. In his 2013 book *Schrödinger's Killer App*, John Dowling calculates that to simulate thulium on a classical computer, you would need to buy up Intel's entire worldwide production of chips for the next 1.5 million years, at a cost of some $600 trillion.

A much quicker alternative would be to simply measure the atom directly. 'Classical computers seem to experience an exponential slowdown when put to simulating entangled quantum systems,' Dowling writes. 'Yet, that same entangled quantum system shows no exponential slowdown when simulating itself. The entangled quantum system acts like a computer that is exponentially more powerful than any classical computer.'

Although we've known all the equations we need to simulate chemistry since the 1930s, we've never had the computing power available to do it. This means that often, when dealing with complex simulations that are intractable for classical computers, the best approach is still to simply try lots of different things in the real world and draw conclusions from observations and experiment. 'We can't really predict how electrons are going to behave right now,' says Zapata's Christopher Savoie. 'If we can get into a world where we're simulating it on a computer, we can be more predictive and do fewer actual laboratory experiments.' It is, he says, as if Airbus were still testing planes by building small-scale models and throwing them into the sky. 'You cannot simulate chemical processes that you're interested in,' says Google's Sergio Boixo. 'With a lot of the low-level materials science and engineering, you're kind of blind.'

To crack these problems, and lots of others like them, chemists, biologists and physicists need to simulate nature – and, exactly as Feynman predicted back in the 1980s, they need computers made from quantum components to help them. In a way, you can think of a quantum computer as a programmable molecule, says Boixo's Google colleague Marissa Giustina. 'It's a system of many parts that behaves according to the rules of quantum mechanics, like a molecule. 'You see a path to connect from there to actually programming chemistry in some senses.'

From farming to pharma

In 2010, Alán Aspuru-Guzik – a professor of chemistry and computer science, and a co-founder of Zapata – teamed up with the quantum physicist Andrew White from the University of Melbourne and others to run one of the first ever quantum chemistry simulations. They picked dihydrogen – a pretty easy molecule, as it goes, and certainly not something that would pose any problems to a classical computer, or even to a physicist with a pen and some paper. Dihydrogen – which is just two hydrogen atoms joined together – was first analysed using the then-new science of quantum mechanics back in 1927. The aim, at this point, was simply to show that quantum computers could be used for this kind of calculation – a proof of concept. Their quantum simulation, which ran on a photon-based quantum device, was able to correctly calculate the strength of the bond between the hydrogen atoms, accurate to six parts in a million.

There are three ways[1] in which quantum computers can help improve our understanding of reactions at the molecular level. The first approach involves building a specific computer to model the problem you're trying to solve – physically recreating the molecule with the right number of qubits corresponding to its actual structure. This kind of machine would be simpler to build, but wouldn't be a computer in the traditional sense – you wouldn't be able to easily reprogram it to tackle different problems.

The second approach involves implementing algorithms that show how a system changes over time. You input the current state of the system, in the form of its wave function, and the level of energy in the system (known as its Hamiltonian, after the mathematician Sir William Rowan Hamilton) and watch it play out over time. These 'Hamiltonian simulations', as they're generally known, have a huge array of potential uses, and could be particularly useful in understanding and predicting complex reactions involving molecules like thulium, where the electrons are highly correlated.

There are a number of active problems like this where classical computers currently struggle, and where quantum computers promise an exponential speed-up. Chemistry challenges just waiting for a quantum computer powerful and reliable enough to crack them range from the extraction of metals by catalysis through to carbon dioxide fixation, which could be used to capture emissions and slow climate change. But the one with the potential for the biggest impact might be fertiliser production. Plants need a healthy supply of nitrogen to grow. The air is full of it, but plants can't actually pull it from the sky themselves, so farmers have to supplement their crops with nitrogen-rich fertiliser produced using the energy-intensive Haber–Bosch process. Forty per cent of the carbon footprint of a loaf of bread comes from producing the nitrogen to make the fertiliser to grow the wheat.[2]

But nature has its own method. Some plants rely on bacteria which use an enzyme called nitrogenase to 'fix' nitrogen from the atmosphere and incorporate it into ammonia. Understanding how this enzyme works would be an important step towards improving the Haber–Bosch process and creating less energy-intensive synthetic fertilisers.

Key to solving that problem is understanding the structure of FeMoco, a complex molecule at the heart of the enzyme that's too difficult for classical computers to model. In 2017, a research team from Microsoft and ETH Zurich demonstrated that a quantum computer with a hundred logical qubits could solve this problem – but acknowledged that they would need up to a million physical qubits to form them.

Another area where Hamiltonian simulations could prove useful is in understanding how plants use the power of the sun. In plants, Photosystem II is a huge, intricate complex of different enzymes that carries out some of the first steps of photosynthesis. Using quantum computers to model the process could help chemists design methods of artificial photosynthesis, enabling them to harness the sun's power to make fuel.

Solar panels themselves are another area where quantum computers could help, by accelerating the search for new materials. This approach could also help to identify new materials for batteries, and superconductors that work at room temperature, which would drive advances in motors, magnets and perhaps even quantum computers themselves.

Zapata is working on a method of finding new materials that uses generative modelling – similar to its work on providing data for machine learning from a small set of real-world data. 'If we have a sample of a hundred things, we can use generative modelling to create things that are similar,' Savoie explains. 'We can use this to do screening of chemical libraries, or to create virtual chemical libraries to find new compounds.'

The ability to potentially identify new compounds is one reason why the medical industry is excited about quantum computing. We have already seen how quantum computers should be able to process data from MRI scans more efficiently and accurately, but they could also save billions in drug design, by enabling companies to quickly identify new compounds, and then simulate their effects without having to synthesise them. Furthermore, quantum computing could help scientists model complex interactions and processes in the body, enabling the discovery of new treatments for diseases such as Alzheimer's, or a quicker understanding of new diseases such as Covid-19. Artificial intelligence is already being used by companies such as DeepMind to gain insight into protein folding – a key facet of growth and disease – and quantum computers will accelerate this effort.

While most of these applications may have to wait for an error-corrected, fault-tolerant quantum computer with thousands or millions of qubits, simulating some natural problems that were previously impossible could, according to some in the field, be within our grasp within the next decade. The first attempts to build quantum computers will be noisy and error-prone, but that could actually make them well suited to simulating nature – molecules in the real world also exist in a world of noise and interference. 'For many applications of quantum devices, such as cryptography, this noise can be a tremendous limitation and lead to unacceptable levels of error,' write Anton Toutov, a Caltech organic chemist, and Prineha Narang, a Harvard materials scientist, in an article for *WIRED*.[3] 'However, for chemistry simulations, the noise would be representative of the physical environment in which both the chemical system (e.g. a molecule) and the quantum device exist. This means that NISQ simulation of a molecule will be noisy, but this noise actually tells you something valuable about how the molecule is behaving in its natural environment.'

When it comes to simulating nature, noise and errors could be a feature, not a bug. Already, small-scale quantum computers equipped with smart, resource-saving algorithms are starting to be used for real-world problems in chemistry and material science.

The key to the universe

In January 2020, researchers at IBM published an early glimpse of how quantum computers could be useful in the NISQ era. Working with the German car manufacturer Daimler on improving batteries for electric vehicles, they used a small-scale quantum computer to simulate the behaviour of three molecules containing lithium, which could be used in the next generation of lithium-sulphur batteries that promise to be more powerful and cheaper than today's power cells. Instead of running a Hamiltonian simulation, which would have required many more qubits than the researchers had access to, they used variational quantum algorithms – the third way quantum computers can simulate nature, and likely to be the most useful in the short and medium term.

Variational quantum algorithms use a hybrid of quantum and classical computers to speed up calculations. In a blog post,[4] Peter Johnson – lead research scientist and founder at Zapata – draws a comparison with the way Google Maps finds you the best route home in a reasonable amount of time. 'The app does not search through all possible routes,' he writes. 'Instead, it ends up searching through a well-motivated subset of routes and partial routes.' What Johnson is saying here is that, rather than going in completely blind, Google's mapping algorithm uses shortcuts and rules of thumb to limit the size of the database it has to search through. You might do something similar if you're looking for a particular house number on an unfamiliar street, and you know that the odd and even numbers are on different sides of the road. Only checking one side of the road halves your search time, with minimal damage to the final result.

Rather than trying to do an entire calculation using a quantum computer, variational quantum algorithms can use a limited number of qubits to make a best guess at the solution with the resources available, and then hand over the result to a classical computer which then decides whether to have another go. Splitting the quantum processing over smaller, independent steps means you can run calculations with fewer, noisier qubits than would otherwise be required.

In 2016, Zapata's Alán Aspuru-Guzik collaborated with Google's research team in Santa Barbara to simulate dihydrogen again, but this time using the search giant's superconducting qubits, and an algorithm known as a 'variational quantum eigensolver'. Again, a quantum computer was able to predict the energy states and bond lengths of the molecule. The technique promises to be easier to scale up to more complex systems without requiring a huge increase in error-correction requirements.

'With this method of the variational quantum eigensolver, one of the things you can do is find the minimum energy of your problem,' says IBM's Heike Riel. 'Typically you have an equation which describes your physical system, and one of the problems you have to solve is to find the minimum energy of this equation.' This method requires far fewer qubits than a full simulation, and has a broad range of applications, from optimisation problems like the travelling salesman, through to chemical reactions where you need to find the ground state (the lowest possible energy level of a system), and ones where an excited state (any other energy level) is of interest – as is the case with photosynthesis and solar energy.

As the number of qubits in early quantum computers increases, their creators are opening up access via the cloud. IBM has its IBM Q network, for instance, while Microsoft has integrated quantum devices into its Azure cloud-computing platform. By combining these platforms with quantum-inspired optimisation algorithms and variable quantum algorithms, researchers could start to see some early benefits of quantum computing in the fields of chemistry and biology within the next few years. In time, Google's Sergio Boixo hopes that quantum computers will be able to tackle some of the existential crises facing our planet. 'Climate change is an energy problem – energy is a physical, chemical process,' he says. 'Maybe if we build the tools that allow the simulations to be done, we can construct a new industrial revolution that will hopefully be a more efficient use of energy.'

But eventually, the area where quantum computers might have the biggest impact is in quantum physics itself. The Large Hadron Collider, the world's largest particle accelerator, collects about 300 gigabytes of data a second as it smashes protons together to try and unlock the fundamental secrets of the universe. To analyse it requires huge amounts of computing power – right now it's split across 170 data centres in 42 countries. Some scientists at CERN – the European Organisation for Nuclear Research – hope quantum computers could help speed up the analysis of data by enabling them to run more accurate simulations before conducting real-world tests. They're starting to develop algorithms and models that will help them harness the power of quantum computers when the devices get good enough to help. 'These are our first steps in quantum computing, but even if we are coming relatively late into the game, we are bringing unique expertise in many fields,' Federico Carminati, a physicist at CERN, told *WIRED* in 2019.[5] 'We are experts in quantum mechanics, which is at the base of quantum computing.'

The Large Hadron Collider's landmark achievement so far is undoubtedly the 2012 discovery of the Higgs boson, an elementary particle whose existence helped confirm some long-held but evidence-light theories of quantum physics. In 2018, physicists from Caltech and the University of Southern California re-analysed the data which led to that discovery using a quantum computer, and managed to replicate the results. It wasn't quicker than a classical device, but it demonstrated that a quantum machine could be used for that type of problem. 'One exciting possibility will be to perform very, very accurate simulations of quantum systems with a quantum computer – which in itself is a quantum system,' said Carminati. 'Other groundbreaking opportunities will come from the blend of quantum computing and artificial intelligence to analyse big data – a very ambitious proposition at the moment, but central to our needs.'

In *Computing with Quantum Cats*, John Gribbin argues that this could be, if not the most important, then certainly the most profound application of quantum computers. 'If we are ever to have a satisfactory "theory of everything" incorporating both quantum theory and gravity,' he writes, 'it is almost certain that it will only be found with the aid of quantum computers to simulate the behaviour of the universe.'

6

The quantum future

The news about Google achieving quantum supremacy leaked out about a month ahead of schedule.

The company had planned a big press day – it had invited journalists to tour the lab in Santa Barbara, wanting to give its scientists a chance to bask in what was, and remains, a remarkable engineering achievement. But not everyone got the memo. In September 2019, a month before the planned reveal, reporters from the *Financial Times*[1] found a copy of the paper that Boixo and his Google colleagues had written about the supremacy experiment – due to be published in the journal *Nature* – freely available to download on an open-access server. By the time the paper – which described how Google's Sycamore chip had taken just 200 seconds to perform a task that would have taken the Summit supercomputer

10,000 years – was actually published in October, the initial excitement had been tempered somewhat. 'It's a stepping stone, but we see stepping stones every year,' says Rob Young. 'I don't think it's a threshold event.'

Researchers at IBM and Microsoft, Google's two main rivals in the race to supremacy, were equally underwhelmed. IBM produced calculations to show that its own supercomputer would have been able to complete the task in two days, not 10,000 years. If this is true, it still means that Google achieved quantum supremacy, but that the feat was not quite as supreme as it first seemed (although the Google team argue that to do it that quickly you'd need to hook your supercomputer up to a nuclear power station).

Instead of quantum supremacy, Microsoft and IBM now prefer to talk about 'quantum advantage' – the point at which quantum computers allow you to do useful things that you couldn't do before. 'We are really focused on providing value and providing a quantum advantage rather than showing supremacy in problems which are not relevant to the industry,' says IBM's Heike Riel. Microsoft's representatives also quickly pivot the conversation away from supremacy, and talk about quantum impact – of finding solutions to some of the world's biggest problems.

To do that, there are four main areas where quantum computing needs to develop over the next few decades: algorithms, hardware, software and skills. A report[2] by the Boston Consulting Group (BCG) divides quantum algorithms, which will be the means by which we find the answers to those big problems, into two main categories: workhorses and purebreds. The latter are things like Shor's algorithm – powerful tools that will offer an exponential speed-up for currently impossible problems, but which require extremely sensitive, specialised hardware with thousands or millions of physical qubits. They're like Formula 1 cars – hugely powerful, but temperamental.

The workhorses, on the other hand, include quantum-approximate optimisation algorithms, and the variational quantum eigensolver that IBM has been using in its battery research with Daimler. These algorithms are the ones that will dominate the NISQ era, as they're flexible enough to run on the error-prone machines we currently have at our disposal. 'Viability is a little bit inversely proportional to value,' is how Boixo puts it.

The challenge for the developers of quantum algorithms isn't only about coming up with something that works, but about proving that it does something useful that you couldn't do on a classical computer. Progress hasn't halted on the classical front either – Google has a parallel team working on ways to improve classical computers so they can compete with its quantum chip, and supercomputers get faster and more powerful every year. 'The dilemma is that very little can be proven about their speed-up performance with respect to classical algorithms until they are put to experimental testing,' write the authors of the BCG report. Grover's algorithm, which doesn't provide an exponential speed-up, but still requires a fault-tolerant quantum computer, is in an unenviable class of its own, being both impractical to run, and not that much more useful than a supercomputer.

That will change as hardware rapidly improves, according to proponents of what's been dubbed the Dowling–Neven Law, named after the quantum physicists John Dowling, who first wrote about the idea of a Moore's Law for quantum computing in his 2013 book, and Hartmut Neven, who led the Google research team which reached supremacy. In June 2019, Neven told *Quanta* magazine[3] that the computational power available in quantum computers was growing at a double exponential rate. 'It looks like nothing is happening, nothing is happening, and then whoops, suddenly you're in a different world,' he said. 'That's what we're experiencing here.'

But to keep that rate of development going, there will need to be big improvements on the hardware side, in terms of both the number of qubits and the ability to manufacture them accurately and at scale. Ideally, companies would be able to crank out qubits with the speed at which they can produce transistors, with Josephson junctions and ion traps rolling off the production line. In reality, the ultra-precise engineering required makes this difficult, and means the failure rate for qubits is unacceptably high.

There are a number of start-ups operating in this area, tapping into the growing funding streams from enterprise and from government. The Finnish start-up IQM, for example, is focused on improving the gate times of quantum hardware so that more operations can be conducted in the short time before a qubit decoheres. 'This is the same as what everyone else is working on,' says IQM's CEO Jan Goetz. 'They're trying to build a system that works with a high success rate and that is scalable at the same time.'

At Microsoft, they're working on ways to miniaturise and harden the control hardware, which currently sits in big racks alongside the cryostat. If they can minimise the number of lines running into the system from outside, they may be able to isolate their qubits better and reduce the amount of noise. Others think the requirement for superconducting qubits to be kept at extremely low temperatures will be an Achilles heel that means they're impossible to scale to the level required. It takes a huge amount of energy and equipment to cool even a small amount of space down to close to absolute zero, and the more that area increases the more the energy required goes up – and the more lines you need going in to control all the additional qubits, which means more leakage and more cooling needed. It might be a problem that's impossible to surmount – which could mean that superconducting qubits are a dead end, and ion traps are the way forward. Or it could be that neither of these technologies will work, and we'll need to find an alternative – or some combination. In December 2020, a group of scientists at the University of Science and Technology in Hefei, China, claimed to have attained quantum supremacy on a photon-based quantum computer that they said was 10,000 times faster than Google's Sycamore chip.

An analysis by *Nature*[4] found that in 2018 there were $173 million of investments in quantum companies, but that the number of deals for hardware firms was vastly outnumbered by investments in quantum software companies, who, it has to be remembered, are often writing algorithms for computers that don't exist yet. That's one of the reasons why some in the industry, including the influential John Preskill, fear a 'quantum winter', where progress will stall because of a lack of developments on the hardware side.

The same thing happened with artificial intelligence, which was first theorised in the 1960s, but had to wait through the 1980s and most of the 1990s for the hardware to catch up before any real progress could be made. That would also track with the famous Gartner hype cycle, which traces the path of new technological developments from invention through the peak of inflated expectations, followed by the trough of disillusionment, to the final plateau of productivity. 'There's so much hype – so people say, "Let's get involved, let's do it,"' said Matthew Brisse, research vice president of quantum computing at Gartner, speaking to *Business Insider* in 2019.[5] 'But then they see that the machines aren't ready yet, and we have to wait five to ten years. There's a real risk of that, so we're monitoring that as well.' Whurley agrees. 'There's this push to get quantum out – it is a revolutionary technology, and all these things that you're hearing from all these major companies are correct,' he says. 'But we're leading people to believe that things may be a lot further mature than they actually are.'

We will probably have to wait a while longer for a fault-tolerant quantum computer capable of running some of the most exciting 'purebred' algorithms. In the meantime, the most likely applications of quantum-based hardware might have very little to do with computing, according to Rhys Lewis of the UK's National Physical Laboratory, which is one of dozens of organisations benefiting from £153 million of government investment into quantum. These could include atomic clocks, for incredibly accurate timekeeping and improved forms of GPS location mapping (which relies on precise timekeeping). The ability to control ions can also be used to make more accurate sensors, which could be useful for 'seeing things which are invisible at the moment, like gravitational fields', says Lewis. Quantum sensors could be used to see what's underground without digging up the road, for testing materials for tiny defects, or to measure the delicate magnetic fields generated by the heart or the brain.

Hello, world

The first computers were programmed by hand, first by rewiring switches and lights, then with holes punched in cards. Today, programmers rarely have to think about the tiny transistors that are actually executing their commands. While physicists and engineers grapple with the hardware problems of quantum, computer scientists are racing ahead, developing the software programs and infrastructure that will sit around quantum devices in the NISQ era and beyond. 'If you have an internal combustion engine, it's not a car,' says Microsoft's Chetan Nayak. 'A car has got to have wheels and a steering wheel and dashboard, and it has to have a GPS system obviously. There's a lot to it, and having fifty per cent or seventy-five per cent of a car is still not a car.'

So now, Google, Microsoft, IBM and others (including the Berkeley-based Rigetti) are all working on the layers that will sit above quantum computers in the same way that compilers and operating systems shield you from the 1s and 0s powering your laptop. 'Right now the programs we write are almost machine code, very close to the hardware,' says Google's Marissa Giustina. 'We don't have any of the high-level tools where you can abstract away the hardware.'

At Microsoft, Krysta Svore, who has a background in computer science, has helped develop Q# (pronounced 'q-sharp'), one of the first programming languages designed specifically for dealing with the quirks of quantum computers of all types. It's designed to be able to easily switch from being run on an ion-trap-based quantum computer to a virtual one running on classical hardware, to one that uses Microsoft's elusive topological qubits, if or when it finally figures out how to make them. 'We know quantum computers are going to develop,' says Svore. 'But that same code is going to endure.'

Google's Cirq and IBM's Qiskit are both open-source frameworks that will help researchers develop algorithms in the NISQ era. As we saw in the last chapter, companies are also powering ahead with commercial applications: IBM is already working with more than 100 companies, including ExxonMobil, Barclays and Samsung, on practical applications; Microsoft has Azure Quantum, which allows its clients to plug into IonQ's trapped-ion quantum computer and superconducting qubits being developed by Connecticut-based QCI. These developments will, says IonQ's Peter Chapman, enable people to start writing the 'Hello, World!' programs for quantum, referring to the simple on-screen message which is one of the first things people learn how to produce when they're first being taught how to code. Eventually, they'll help people who don't have a degree in quantum physics or computer science (or both) access the intricacies of quantum devices. Skills are the final piece of the puzzle. 'There are no university programmes,' says Giustina. 'There's not a field yet. To reach this vision we'll need a lot more expertise in that programming.'

There are lots of parallels between the early days of quantum computing and classical computing – some of the early devices even look similar, with their tangles of wires reaching from floor to ceiling. But where classical computers were confined to academic labs and military facilities for decades and only really reached the masses with the rise of personal computing in the 1990s, quantum computers will be readily accessible to all – not in person, but via the cloud. That could mean a vast difference in the speed at which new applications can be developed, as programmers and even interested amateurs can access qubits to simply mess around with and try out ideas.

Eventually, though, the end user of a quantum computer will probably be unaware that they're actually using one.

You'll never have a quantum chip in your own device – instead, you'll access their powers via the cloud. Quantum processors of various different types – superconducting, trapped-ion, simulated – will form part of an arsenal of technologies that are automatically selected. 'Our vision is you and me having a problem and we just use the normal software we use, and then the cloud behind, which has access to all these kinds of computers and decides which one to run the problem on,' says IBM's Riel.

Of course, it's unlikely that the average person will ever need to directly interact with a quantum computer, in the same way that you don't access the world's fastest supercomputers to check email or do word-processing today. There'll never be an iPhone Q with a quantum chip inside. But quantum computers could help find the battery materials that help that phone run for longer, and the optimum circuit design for maximum efficiency, and the best search algorithm for its web browser, and the quickest route for the drone to take when it delivers it to your door.

Quantum advantage could be five years away, or five decades. There's a danger of overhyping the achievements so far – it's still possible that there is some fundamental barrier that will prevent the number of qubits being scaled up, or that the noise will simply become insurmountable above a certain level. Artur Ekert, whose talk in 1994 kickstarted the race to quantum supremacy and helped get the field to this point, thinks we'll still need some major technological breakthrough akin to the development of the transistor, which transformed conventional computers from the 1960s onwards. With quantum, we are not in the days of rival chipmakers battling to produce the best possible hardware; we're in the days of vacuum tubes and mechanical gates, and researchers wondering whether the thing they're trying to do is even possible. In one sense, Ekert confides that he actually hopes it isn't possible. 'It would be an even more wonderful scenario if we cannot build a quantum computer for truly fundamental reasons – if actually it's impossible, because of some new, truly fundamental laws of physics,' he says.

A practical, error-corrected quantum computer could change the world. It could revolutionise medicine, accelerate artificial intelligence and upend cryptography, by using the uncertainty of quantum physics to its advantage. But the battle to build one could reveal fundamental truths about the universe itself. 'This is not a competition between companies,' reflects the Google quantum researcher Yu Chen. 'It's our technology against nature.'

Glossary

Classical computer

Almost every computer ever made – from wartime codebreakers to the phone in your pocket – essentially works in the same way, with millions of tiny switches called bits.

Decoherence

When a qubit falls out of the delicate state of superposition because of interference or noise from the environment, it is said to have decohered.

Entanglement

The way two particles can become linked, or 'entangled', so that anything you do to one happens to the other, no matter the distance separating them.

QUANTUM COMPUTING

Moore's Law

In 1965 Gordon Moore, the co-founder of Intel, predicted a doubling of the number of switches (known as transistors) able to fit on a chip every two years.

NISQ

An acronym for 'noisy intermediate scale quantum' – a term coined by the physicist John Preskill – referring to an era where quantum computers exist, but they're not yet robust enough to fulfil their full promise.

Quantum advantage

The term preferred by IBM and Microsoft, which refers to the point at which quantum computers can do useful things that wouldn't be possible any other way.

Quantum supremacy

The term coined in 2012 by the physicist John Preskill to describe the point at which quantum computers can do things classical computers can't (regardless of whether those things are useful).

Qubit

Instead of representing just 1 or 0, like a bit in an ordinary computer chip, a qubit – short for 'quantum bit' – can represent both at the same time.

Superconducting qubit

Google and IBM are building 'superconducting qubits', which rely on extreme cold and a ring of metal with a nanometre gap called a Josephson junction, which changes the way electrons behave. Microwave pulses are used to flip the qubit between states. IBM varies the frequency of these pulses to adjust for manufacturing variations, while Google uses a magnetic field to 'tune' the qubits.

Superposition

The state of being both 1 and 0 at the same time is called superposition – think of it as a flipped coin that hasn't landed yet.

Topological qubit

Superconducting qubits only last for fractions of a second. At Microsoft, they're working on 'topological qubits', which store the information in several places at once. This should make them last longer, and mean they're more powerful – but they might be impossible to make.

Variational quantum algorithm

Variational quantum algorithms use a hybrid of quantum and classical computers to speed up calculations. Rather than trying to do a whole calculation using a quantum computer with limited qubits, variational quantum algorithms make a best guess at the solution with the resources available, and then hand over the result to a classical computer. Splitting the quantum processing over smaller, independent steps means you can run calculations with fewer, noisier qubits than would otherwise be required.

Acknowledgements

This book is intended to be a primer to quantum computing for people who don't have a background in maths or physics. I've tried to avoid using mathematical formulae and complex diagrams as far as possible, and aimed to be clear and simple without oversimplifying. This was tricky – one of the first things an interviewee ever told me about quantum computers was that they 'defy analogy'.

So, although any errors and omissions are mine alone, I've relied throughout on the patience of experts. I'm particularly grateful to the people who gave up their time to be interviewed for the book, to set up visits to research labs, or to answer my questions over email over the course of several months. Thank you to all my interviewees, but particularly to Rob Young and Andrea Rocchetto for poring over the first draft, and to my editor, Nigel Wilcockson.

Bibliography

Brown, J., *The Quest for the Quantum Computer*, (Touchstone, 2001)

Dowling, J., *Schrodinger's Killer App: Race to Build the World's First Quantum Computer* (CRC Press, 2013)

Gribbin, J., *Computing with Quantum Cats: From Colossus to Qubits* (Transworld Digital, 2013)

Johnson, G., *A Shortcut Through Time: The Path to a Quantum Computer* (Vintage Digital, 2011)

Notes

Notes to Introduction pages 1–7

1   https://www.discovermagazine.com/technology/the-best-computer-in-all-possible-worlds

2   https://quantum.country/qcvc

3   https://www.newscientist.com/article/2220968-its-official-google-has-achieved-quantum-supremacy/

Notes to 1 What is quantum computing? pages 9–29

1   https://www.nytimes.com/2019/10/30/opinion/google-quantum-computer-sycamore.html

2   https://www.nature.com/articles/nphys2258

3   https://physicsworld.com/a/researchers-make-single-atom-transistor/#:~:text=Researchers%20in%20Australia%20have%20created,creation%20of%20atomic%2Dscale%20electrodes.

4   *The Quest for the Quantum Computer*, p. 19.

Notes to 2 Building the impossible   pages 31–53

1   *Computing with Quantum Cats*, p. 217.

2   https://journals.aps.org/prl/abstract/10.1103/PhysRevLett.74.4091

3   p. 255.

4   p. 235.

5   https://www.technologyreview.com/2020/02/26/916744/quantum-computer-race-ibm-google/

Notes to 3 Exponential power   pages 55–75

1   https://www.youtube.com/watch?v=TlQABw_gCF4

2   https://www.wired.co.uk/article/quantum-computers-ibm-cern

3   https://www.wired.co.uk/article/ibm-barclays-banking-quantum-computing

Notes to 4 Cracking the code   pages 77–96

1   https://www.cnas.org/publications/reports/quantum-hegemony

2   https://www.nap.edu/catalog/25196/quantum-computing-
     progress-and-prospects

3   https://csrc.nist.gov/projects/post-quantum-
     cryptography/workshops-and-timeline

4   https://www.bbc.co.uk/news/science-environment-40294795

Notes to 5 Simulating nature   pages 97–114

1   https://www.nap.edu/catalog/25196/quantum-computing-
     progress-and-prospects

2   https://cen.acs.org/articles/95/i43/Chemistry-quantum-
     computings-killer-app.html

3   https://www.wired.com/story/opinion-noisy-quantum-
     computers-chemistry-problems/

4   https://www.zapatacomputing.com/variational-what-now/

5   https://www.wired.co.uk/article/quantum-computers-ibm-cern

Notes to 6 The quantum future   pages 115–130

1   https://www.ft.com/content/b9bb4e54-dbc1-11e9-8f9b-
     77216ebe1f17

2   https://www.bcg.com/publications/2018/next-decade-
    quantum-computing-how-play

3   https://www.quantamagazine.org/does-nevens-law-
    describe-quantum-computings-rise-20190618/

4   https://www.nature.com/articles/d41586-019-02935-4

5   https://www.businessinsider.com/vcs-are-investing-in-
    quantum-startups-but-expect-a-quantum-winter-2019-
    3?r=US&IR=T

Index